Clickety-Clack, Something to Pack

An Enchanting Puzzle Game

Verse by
Antony Lishak

Pictures by
Ian Penney

ORCHARD BOOKS

Also by Ian Penney
A Shop Full of Kittens
Under the Sun and Over the Moon
(Verse by Kevin Crossley-Holland)

For Eleanor   *For Sam*
from Ian   *A.L.*

ORCHARD BOOKS
96 Leonard Street, London EC2A 4RH
Orchard Books Australia
14 Mars Road, Lane Cove, NSW 2066
1 85213 333 3
First published in Great Britain 1992
Text copyright © Antony Lishak 1992
Illustrations copyright © Ian Penney 1992
The right of Antony Lishak to be identified as the author and
Ian Penney as the illustrator of this work
has been asserted by them in accordance with the
Copyright, Designs and Patents Act, 1988.
A CIP catalogue record for this book is available from the British Library.
Printed in Belgium

Here is a suitcase. Now, what will you pack?

One model train going clickety-clack,
That trundles along on a rickety track.

Here is a suitcase. Now, what will you pack?
One model train going clickety-clack, and . . .

Two runaway rabbits, who just want to play.
They're too quick for catching and packing away.

Here is a suitcase. Now, what will you pack?
One model train,

Two runaway rabbits, who just want to play, and . . .

Three elegant clocks that go clatter and click,
A collection of tocks and a clamour of ticks.

Here is a suitcase. Now, what will you pack?
One model train,

Two runaway rabbits,

Three elegant clocks that go clatter and click, and . . .

Four funny hats to put on your head,
Outdoors in all weathers or indoors instead.

Here is a suitcase. Now, what will you pack?
One model train,

Two runaway rabbits,

Three elegant clocks,

Four funny hats to put on your head, and . . .

Five climbing kites that soar high in the sky,
A spiralling box and some beetles that fly.

Here is a suitcase. Now, what will you pack?
One model train,

Two runaway rabbits,

Three elegant clocks,

Four funny hats,

Five climbing kites that soar high in the sky, and . . .

Six useful jugs, each with handle and lip,
For carefully pouring out something to sip.

Here is a suitcase. Now, what will you pack?

One model train,

Two runaway rabbits,

Three elegant clocks,

Four funny hats,

Five climbing kites,

Six useful jugs,
each with handle and lip,
and . . .

Seven bouncing balls to catch or to throw,
Roll, hit or bat them, and just watch them go.

Here is a suitcase. Now, what will you pack?

 One model train,

 Two runaway rabbits,

 Three elegant clocks,

 Four funny hats,

 Five climbing kites,

 Six useful jugs,

 Seven bouncing balls
to catch or to throw,
and . . .

Eight gleaming toy cars with chromium wheels
And bonnets and bumpers that almost look real.

Here is a suitcase. Now, what will you pack?

 One model train,

 Two runaway rabbits,

Three elegant clocks,

 Four funny hats,

 Five climbing kites,

 Six useful jugs,

 Seven bouncing balls,

 Eight gleaming toy cars
with chromium wheels,
and . . .

Nine cuddly animals to hug close in bed,
From a furry giraffe to a balding old ted.

Here is a suitcase. Now, what will you pack?

 One model train,

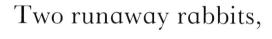 Two runaway rabbits,

 Three clocks,

 Four hats,

 Five kites,

 Six jugs,

 Seven balls,

 Eight toy cars,

 Nine cuddly animals
to hug close in bed, and . . .

Ten beautiful shells gathered up from the beach,
Jewels of the seas within everyone's reach.

Now, can you remember what you must pack?

Ten

Nine

Eight

Seven

Six

Five

Four

Three

Two

One

Those rabbits were there just a moment ago.
Where are they now: does anyone know?

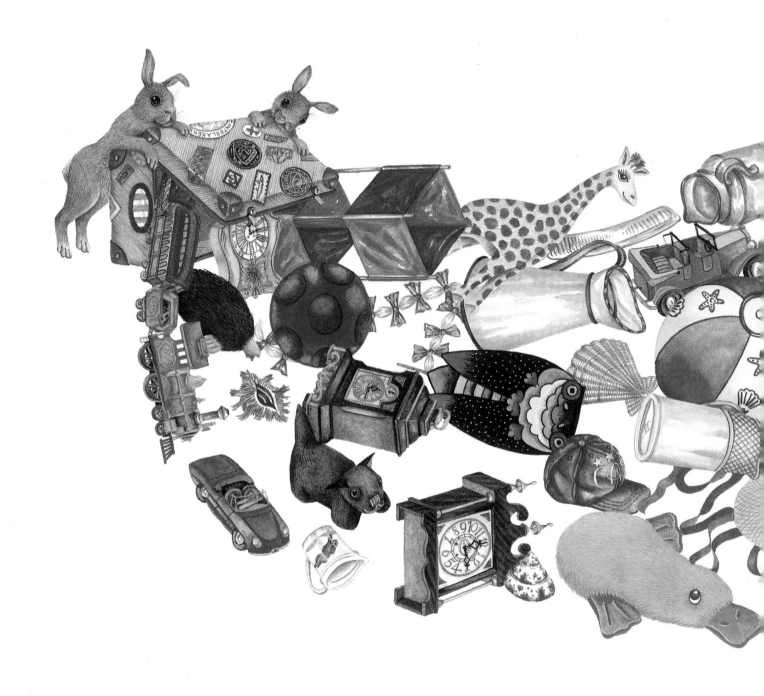

Those runaway rabbits!
Just look what they've done.

We'll have to go back and start over again.
Now, where is that rickety clickety train?